Personalise the blank cards or choose from the other cards in the pack.

Includes:

We're having a baby!

Pregnancy cards from 4 weeks to due date

The first scan

Felt the first kick

My cravings

First day in maternity clothes

First baby buy

Your first outfit

Our family now you are here

Your cards and gifts

Your nursery

Ensure you use a wipe-clean pen to write on the blank cards.

D0187901

Me when I found out I was having

you

Date:

We're having a baby!

Date:

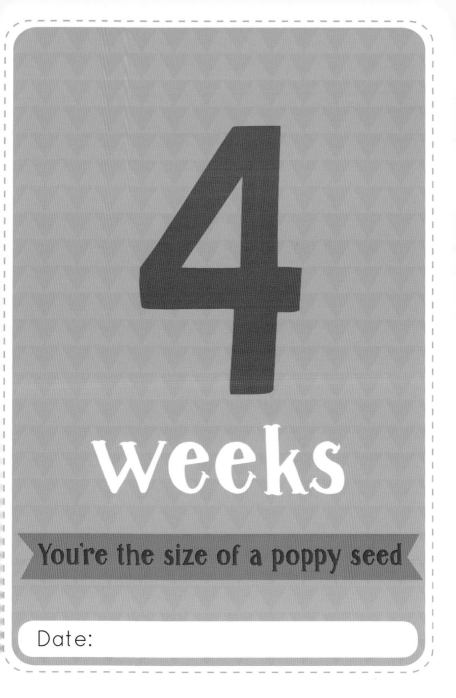

4
weeks

You're the size of a poppy seed

Date:

8

weeks

Do you think people can tell?

Date:

. . . .

weeks

Date:

The secret is out!

Date:

The first scan

Date:

20

weeks

Halfway there!

Date:

The second scan

Date:

24
weeks

Over halfway!

Date:

28
weeks

12 weeks to go!

Date:

32

weeks

Not much longer!

Date:

36
weeks

Getting close!

Date:

Due date

C'mon baby!

Date:

Ready to pop!

Date:

First time
I laughed
and let out
a little
wee

Date:

Felt the

first

kick

Date:

It's a
girl!

Date:

It's a
boy!

Date:

It's twins!

Date:

My cravings

Date:

First
baby
buy

Date:

Your first outfit

Date:

Our family before you were born

Date:

Our family now you are here

Date:

I'm going to be

....

Date:

Your cards and gifts

Date:

Your nursery

Date:

The day you came home

Date:

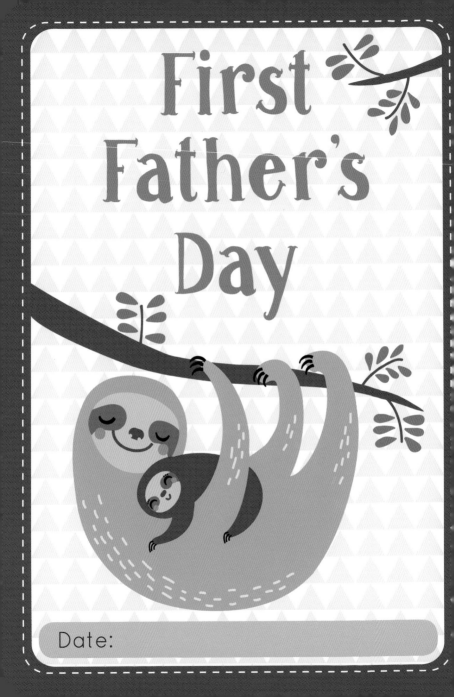

First
Father's
Day

Date:

First Mother's Day

Date:

Mummy's
favourite names

 girl

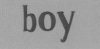 boy

....

....

....

....

....

 Date:

Daddy's
favourite names

girl	boy

....

....

....

....

....

Date:

A bit about you

Name:

Weight:

Length:

Born:

Time:

Your first night at home

Date:

You and

....

Date:

You and

....

Date:

Today
you

....

....

Date:

Today you

Date:

First time

Date:

A message

from us to you

....

....

....

....

....

....

....

Date: